Georg Philipp Telemann
1681 – 1767

Don Quixote Suite

6 Pieces for Descant Recorder and Keyboard
6 Stücke für Sopranblockflöte und Klavier

Edited by / Herausgegeben von
Gwilym Beechey

ED 13219
ISMN 979-0-2201-3087-8

www.schott-music.com

Mainz · London · Berlin · Madrid · New York · Paris · Prague · Tokyo · Toronto
© 2008 SCHOTT MUSIC Ltd, London · Printed in Germany

ED 13219
British Library Cataloguing-in-Publication Data.
A catalogue record for this book is available from the British Library
ISMN M-2201-3087-8
ISBN 978-1-84761-138-3

Music setting by Figaro
Printed in Germany S&Co.8491

Contents

Telemann's *Don Quixote Suite* for strings and continuo is thought to have been composed at Frankfurt in about 1720 and contains eight movements. The influences on the work were clearly French, the movements consisting of a *Lullian Overture* and a number of dances and programmatic pieces, all with French titles. Six of the latter have been selected for this arrangement of movements for descant recorder and keyboard.

Tempi in brackets are editorial, as also are suggestions for mood given by dynamics. The continuo may be played on a harpsichord or piano, and the presence of a string bass is highly desirable if the former instrument is used. Nos. 4 and 5 may be played singly, but they are preferable as a pair. A number of ornaments have been suggested, and further decorations may be added as desired, particularly for the repeats of the sections of the movement.

G.E.B.

Don Quixote Suite

Edited and arranged by/
Herausgegeben und bearbeitet von
Gwilym Beechey

G. P. Telemann
(1681–1767)

1. Le Reveil de Quixotte

2. Son Attaque des Moulins à Vent

Georg Philipp Telemann
1681 – 1767

Don Quixote Suite

6 Pieces for Descant Recorder and Keyboard
6 Stücke für Sopranblockflöte und Klavier

Edited by / Herausgegeben von
Gwilym Beechey

ED 13219
ISMN 979-0-2201-3087-8

Descant Recorder / Sopranblockflöte

www.schott-music.com

Mainz · London · Berlin · Madrid · New York · Paris · Prague · Tokyo · Toronto
© 2008 SCHOTT MUSIC Ltd, London · Printed in Germany

Descant Recorder

Don Quixote Suite

Edited and arranged by/
Herausgegeben und bearbeitet von
Gwilym Beechey

G. P. Telemann
(1681–1767)

1. Le Reveil de Quixotte

2. Son Attaque des Moulins à Vent

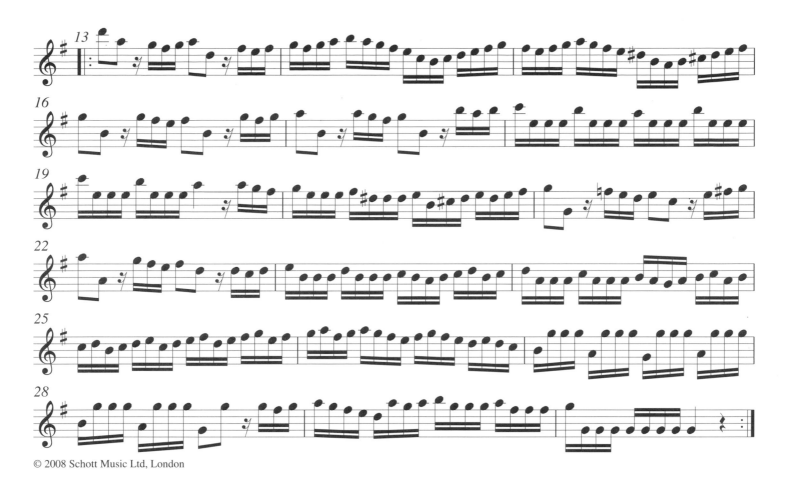

3. Les Soupirs amoureux après le Princesse Dulcinée

(Affettuoso e dolce)

4. Le Galope de Rosinante

(Allegro moderato)

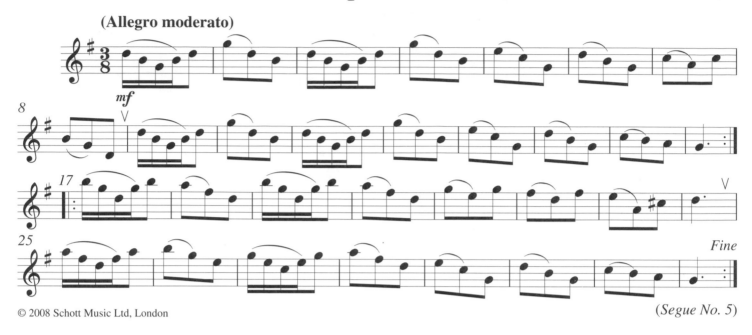

(Segue No. 5)

5. Celui d'Ane de Sanche

Doux

Le Galope de Rosinante
da capo

6. Le Couché de Quixotte

(Alla bourée)

D.C. al Fine

S&Co.8491 Printed in Germany

3. Les Soupirs amoureux après le Princesse Dulcinée

4. Le Galope de Rosinante

(Segue No. 5)

5. Celui d'Ane de Sanche

Le Galope de Rosinante
da capo

12

6. Le Couché de Quixotte

S&Co.8491 Printed in Germany